The Journal of

Mrs Soane's Dog

FANNY

For Derek Martin

1931 – 2009

The Journal of Mrs Soane's Dog

FANNY

1813 - 1820

by Herself

AND MIRABEL CECIL

ILLUSTRATED BY FRANCESCA MARTIN

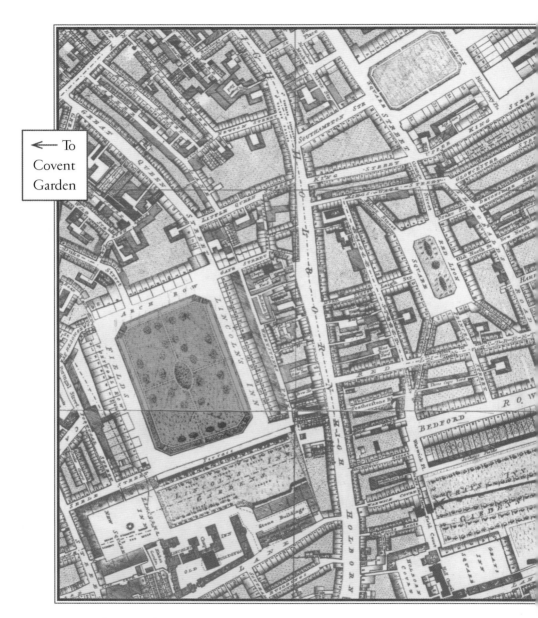

← To Covent Garden

Map showing the principal locations in Fanny's journal,
based on Horwood's map of London of 1819

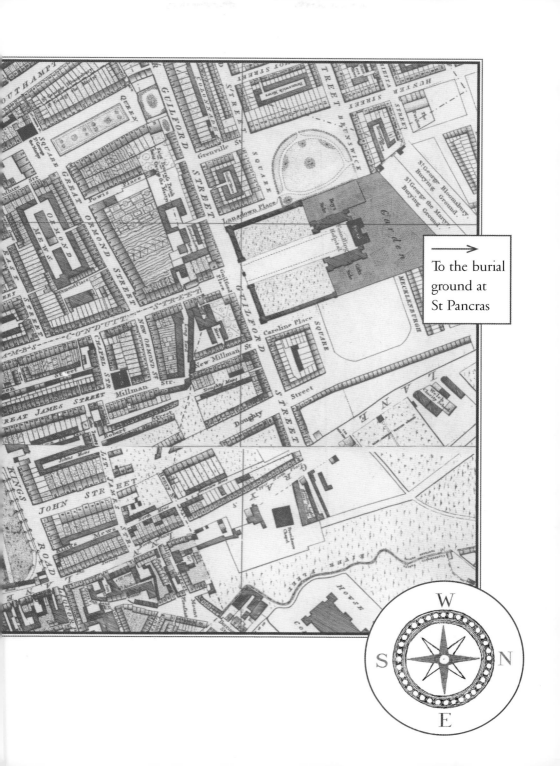

To the burial
ground at
St Pancras

Contents

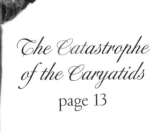

Editor's Introduction

Sir John Soane loved surprises. His house was full of them – and it still is! Its dark corners, its hidden cupboards, and its mysterious panels hold all kinds of secrets: the story on the following pages is one of them. How did it come to be written? Where was it discovered?

But let us begin at the beginning, here at Number 13 Lincoln's Inn Fields in the middle of London. John Soane lived in this house with his wife and their two sons, until the boys grew up and moved away from home. There was another member of the family here, too: **Frances**, or **Fanny**, Mrs Soane's beloved dog and constant companion.

*So delightful and intelligent a creature was Fanny
that I suppose I should not have been surprised that
when several pieces of paper were found hidden in this
house and I pieced them all together, they made up
Fanny's Journal, an account of her life here until
her death in 1820. I hope that you will enjoy reading
it as much as I enjoyed editing it and my friend
Francesca Martin enjoyed painting the pictures to
illustrate it.*

Mirabel Cecil
London, 2010

Our House at Number 13

To MANY PEOPLE THIS HOUSE is scary, but not to me. I have lived here at Number 13, or next door at Number 12, all my life, since about the year 1803, and I love it here. It was my Master, the famous architect, John Soane, and my Mistress, Mrs Soane, who named me Frances, and I'm called Fanny, or Fan, for short. Next door, where we used to live, is my good friend Mew, the cat. He and I have long been friends, and his Master, Mr Tyndale, is great friends with my Master and Mistress. He is a very handsome creature (Mew, that is, not Mr Tyndale, who is just an ordinary chap) with beautiful dark brown stripes on his golden fur, eyes the colour of amber (or jade, in some lights), and long white whiskers, of which he is very proud. He has a most expressive tail, which he can curl at the end when he feels especially jaunty.

His paws are black on the inside, and, when he rolls over on his back and stretches out, he shows the dark brown spots on his tummy.

As you can see looking around you, Master loves collecting 'stones and bones', as I think of them – anything promising that comes his way or catches his fancy.

He is happy for this house to be a museum as well as the family home. He likes people coming to look at his pictures and drawings and antiquities, and lots of people do come: this is one of the most famous houses in London! I'm not sure my Mistress shares this passion for collecting. Although she never says so, I think her heart sinks when yet another cart carrying a statue or a large chunk of stone draws up outside the house.

There are indeed many ancient fragments here: of stony faces, snarling lions, writhing snakes. Some pieces are huge – the life-size statue of the god Apollo, under the Dome in the centre, was so big that the back wall of the house had to be taken down to get him inside! The dust and mess were tremendous, but there he now stands, a handsome fellow, admired by all. Master likes to show off his collection in shadowy half-light, with flickering candles and nothing too brightly lit. As a result, you never know what might lurk in dark corners or might greet you down a passageway.

The Catastrophe of the Caryatids

ONE DAY JUST LATELY a cart drew up carrying two elegant ladies lying on a bed of straw. They're called *caryatids*, and they were to stand on the outside of the house. These beautiful stone creatures were hoisted up on great stout ropes, one on either side of the front of the house. Everyone went outside into the Square to admire them. Mew and I decided to take a closer look, so we went back through the house, upstairs to the second floor, where we jumped out of the window to the ledge where the caryatids now stood.

Mew and I sat there in the twilight, discussing the two ladies. Sitting at the feet of one of them, we looked up at their pale costumes, glimmering in the half-light.

Suddenly, 'Bet you can't climb up her,' said he.

'Bet I can,' said I at once.

'Right! Let's climb one each.'

'You go first,' I replied, thinking that I could perhaps pretend to go up and Mew would never know. For I hate heights: I like to know that I can get back from wherever I find myself, either by the way I came, or by another way. Mew isn't like that. He's always shinning up trees in the Square garden and jeering at me from on high when I won't join him. Now he was determined to climb up and see what life looked like from atop one of these ladies.

Cats are so nosy; there is an expression, isn't there – 'curiosity killed the cat'. Well, on this occasion it nearly did.

Mew got up all right: ''s easy as peasy,' he called down at me from atop the statue's head. It had begun to drizzle, so after a little while of encouraging me to climb up too, he said, 'Right, I'm coming down.'

There was a pause; then he said, 'I'm coming down *now*.'

Another pause, then in a wavering voice he called, 'HELP! I can't get down!'

I looked up through the gathering darkness and misty drizzle. I could just make out this damp and furry shape, looking like one of Master's wigs on its wig-stand, except that this shape had huge scared eyes and a twitching tail. I couldn't help laughing at him. 'Come on, Mew-kin, just slide yourself down.'

But he whimpered, 'I can't slide, it's slippery, and I can't make out where to go.'

'Look, I'll break your fall,' I said, with a show of gallant resolution. 'I'll lie at the bottom, and you can fall on me.' (Not many friends I'd make *that* kind of offer to.)

But Mew had lost his nerve.

'I can't, I can't jump – I don't know how far it is.'

It was then that I realised that Mew had got himself well and truly stuck. He cried piteously, and I yapped, but no one could hear us up there. I also recollected that the house was empty. Master was out discussing a new building with a client, and my Mistress was at the theatre with Mew's Master and Mistress, Mr and Mrs Tyndale. I decided to go indoors in search of whatever help I could find. I went back through the window we had used to get out – no one about – so I went right down into the basement to find Will, the footman. I barked and pulled at his sleeve. He, thinking I was hungry, brought me some leftovers from dinner.

They were delicious, and I ate them, but that was not what I had come for. He didn't understand why I kept on yapping and running to the bottom of the stairs and back. I think he was more interested in the letter he was writing to his sweetheart in the country.

Finally, after what seemed like hours, my Mistress returned. I rushed up to the front door to greet her.

'There, there, Fan,' said she, picking me up and cradling me in her arms, 'I've not been out long. Shush now.'

I had to get her to come upstairs at once. I tugged at her skirt – and yapped – and tugged – and she, being my Mistress, knew immediately that something was the matter, and followed me upstairs to where we'd climbed outside.

I scratched at the window sill, jumped up, and scratched some more, to make her look out and see Mew clinging to the top of the stone lady. Will, who'd followed us up, went and fetched a ladder, which he passed out of the window.

Mew crawled indoors, damp and bedraggled, his fine tail dripping, his ears flattened. My Mistress got an old sheet and dried him off, and he sat in front of her bedroom fire and fluffed himself up again.

My Mistress comforted him. 'There, Mew, all's well now; Fanny, brave dog, brave girl.' At that moment Master came back, and she told him all about the adventure: she made me out to be the Heroine of the Hour! Master was most impressed. He patted me and put down a saucer of milk for Mew. Then he escorted Mew safely back home to Number 12 next door, and we all settled down for the night.

The two ladies, whom we call *Carrie* and *Attid*, are still there, gazing out across the square – but we have never been tempted to climb up them again.

My Family at Number 13

THE ROOM WHERE I SLEEP is Mrs Soane's bedroom, up on the second floor. My bed is under the window and if I climb on to a stool and put my paws up on the window sill, I can look out over the garden in the Square, and beyond it, over the rooftops of London. As well as blinds, there are wooden shutters on either side of the windows to keep out the light and the cold. In the morning when our housemaid Sally comes in to open the shutters and to wake my Mistress and light the fire in the room, she often brings me biscuits too.

This is at about eight o'clock; then Sally and I go downstairs and out across the road into the garden, where I usually meet Mew and we exchange news and gossip about the Square.

Then it's back across the road for Sally and me, taking care to avoid the carriages that are already thundering around the Square, and down the stairs outside the front of the house into what's known as the 'area'. The door here leads into the kitchen in the basement.

Down here Cook reigns. Cooky and I have a somewhat uneasy relationship. She suspects me of nicking food when she's not looking. (I'm saying nothing!) What I do know is that she has a kitchen cat, called Mouser, a great big fellow, but he doesn't catch as many mice as Mew – and often claims as his own what Mew has caught.

At this early hour of the day the kitchen is busy: delivery men draw up outside with their carts, and the milkmaid comes down the area steps, whistling, with her twin pails of milk. She is a favourite with Mew, but for me it's time to run upstairs to the breakfast room for breakfast with my Mistress.

Sometimes Master is there, usually in a hurry to be off to work to see his clients. He doesn't talk much, being busy making notes in the little books he always carries about with him. He writes in them first from one end, then from the other. When the two sides meet in the middle, they're full. Their two boys, John and George, are grown up now and have left home, so we don't see much of them.

So Mrs Soane is often by herself, with just me for company; she tells me what a good companion I am to her. Well, so is she to me. I could not wish for a gentler, kinder, better-tempered, more generous Mistress than she is.

Fanny and Mew join Mr and Mrs Soane in the breakfast room.

Matthew

At the back of Number 13, a narrow wooden staircase, which visitors seldom see, twists up from the ground floor. It leads to the Drawing Office, one of my favourite places of all – although it cannot be called in the least bit comfortable. This is where the boys work who come to learn how to be an architect, like Master. There is a stove here, and if you sit next to it, part of you warms up, but the other part, away from the fire, stays cold. If the Office is full, some boys don't get near it at all.

Skylights here let in as much daylight as possible to draw by. I like the tools they use for their work: shiny brass compasses and dividers, ivory rulers, fine-pointed

pencils. And I like the smell of the ink, kept in clear glass inkwells into which they dip their long quill pens.

I like following the pens as they move along the page, with a squeak when they go down to make a capital letter – such as *F* for Fanny – and a different sort of squeak when they go upwards – *M* for Mew, for instance – and other sorts of squeaks when they make drawings. Sometimes I chew the feather, but the boys don't like that because the ink is sure to make a blot and spoil the page so that Master gets cross and makes them do the work all over again in their own time.

My special friend in the Drawing Office is a pupil called Matthew Pool. He is a small boy, pale and cold: his fingers are cold, his nose is cold (and generally has a drip on the end), his ears are cold, and his eyes are pale blue and watery – but his heart is warm.

The other boys tease him and sing: 'Matthew Pool, white-faced fool!' He is white-faced because he is always cold and mostly hungry. On his thin fingers and his thin toes are chilblains. These horrid red swellings come because he is so-o-o co-o-o-ld. They itch and irritate him, and he can't get rid of them in the wintertime. His mother is widowed, so he has no father, and this is the first time he has been away from home; he misses his brothers and sisters. He lives a long way from London, and he can scarcely ever afford to go back to see them.

He talks to me in his soft country voice, which sounds different from London voices. He gets teased for his accent as well, when he says things like 'e laid it on proper' when Master criticises his work, or tells him off if he is late. Then the other boys leap around crying, 'What did he do, Matthew? Did 'e lay it on proper?', thinking themselves wonderfully funny.

Anyway, he says to me, 'You'd think, wouldn't you, Fanny, that I would be used to the cold, coming from Norfolk on the North Sea coast. But perhaps it's because

my clothes are thin, or because I lodge in a room on my own, I can *never* seem to get warm.'

One rainy morning I found him, head down on the drawing table, crying with cold and loneliness. His feet were wet because his shoes leak and he can't afford to have them mended, so he'd stuffed the holes with paper, which had got all soggy, and his fingers ached because his woollen mittens were sodden. Gently, I tugged his stockings to get them off. I hung them on the bottom rung of his stool (like Sally the housemaid does with hers) in front of the stove

30

to dry, with his mittens. Then I raced as quickly as I could to Master's wardrobe, where I found some old sheepskin slippers, large and furry. I carried them to Matthew to wear whilst his stockings dried. Ever since then he keeps these slippers under the table so he'll always have something warm and dry to put on whatever the weather. If the other boys laugh and call him 'hairy toes', I yap at them, and snap at their ankles – they don't like that at all!

Sometimes I manage to filch a hot potato from the kitchen when Cooky's baked some in the oven (the coachmen use them to warm their hands in their greatcoat pockets). I rush upstairs with it and slip it into Matthew's jacket pocket.

'Thanks, Fanny,' he says, 'I'll eat that tonight for supper. Mamma's sent me some fresh butter from the country and six eggs from our hens.'

If Cook's having one of her Baking Days, which she likes to do once or twice a month, I can even sneak a meat patty out from under her nose and make off with it for Matthew. Last time I did that, though, she caught me as she was coming back into the kitchen and I was trying to scamper past. 'Stop, thief!' she yelled, and bustled after me, but she was too breathless to catch me. She threw her shoe at me up the stairs but missed me by miles. Mew very sportingly, we thought, caught a large mouse and laid it neatly across her

feet as she snored by the fire after supper that evening to make it up to her and to show that I was no common thief. She didn't appreciate this tribute as much as we expected.

Matthew drew a picture of me: 'Fanny in the Drawing Office', he wrote underneath, and signed it *Matthew*. I thought my Mistress would like it, so I took it to her, and she admired it very much. 'But who is Matthew?' she wondered. So I tugged at her skirt, and she came with me to the Drawing Office, where I led her to Matthew. Poor boy, that day he was particularly pale and red-eyed, his nose was running and he was coughing too.

'Why, it's Matthew Pool,' she said and talked to him about his mother and his family, whom she knew because Master had been doing some work near the Pools' village in Norfolk.

She felt sorry for Matthew and asked him about his lodgings and lots of other questions. I know that from now on she will keep an eye on him and make sure that he has enough to eat and that his clothes are mended. She has even given him some of young John's clothes, a warm overcoat that he had outgrown, and a long woolly muffler as well. I have never seen Matthew grin so widely as he did on the day he put those on, and I wouldn't be surprised if he put them across his bed in his lodging house at night as extra covers.

The Destruction of Stonehenge

MEW OFTEN JOINS me in the Drawing Office. It's cosy up there with the boys, listening to the gentle hiss of the stove and the 'whoosh!' of the cinders as they fall and the rain pattering on the glass of the skylights above. When the light fades, one of the boys lights the lamps, which throw out a golden glow across the crowded work table and make the shadows lengthen throughout the room.

When all the pupils have left for the day, we sometimes stay there in the remaining warmth of the stove. But one evening last week there was a disaster. Mew saw a mouse cheekily scurrying right across the room, and, without thinking twice, he boldly leapt after it across the table, hurtling straight through a model of some ruins, which sat upon it. The ruins scattered everywhere.

Unfortunately, they are not just any old ruins, but a model of Stonehenge, which, as you know, is one of the world's oldest 'buildings'! To us, and perhaps to you, they might look like higgledy-piggledy stones in any sort of order, or none, but to Master they are very important, and their order matters very much indeed.

Well, Mew and I were on our own, and I knew that there was no point in either of us trying to put the model back as it was because we'd only get it wrong. So, next morning, we went into the Drawing Office really early and waited for Matthew to arrive. We pushed all the pieces together and stood by them expectantly, sure that so clever a lad could work out the arrangement of this mysterious ancient monument.

When he came in, it didn't take him a moment to grasp what had happened. 'Oh dear,' he said, 'this is a tricky one.' He began to piece the model together when Master's unmistakable step was heard upon the stairs. 'Quick, Matthew,' I whimpered, but it was too late: Master was in the room and saw the mess at once.

There was nothing else for it – we had to take the blame. Matthew didn't give us away, but I barked and pawed Master's leg, and Mew purred and rubbed against his other leg, so that he knew that it was our fault and he wasn't cross with Matthew.

Luckily, Stonehenge is one of the ancient buildings the pupils have to draw as one of their exercises in perspective and proportion, so Matthew got out the drawing he'd done and followed it to put the model together again. It took him quite a while, but he didn't complain, and I filched a jam tart from the kitchen to keep him going in this fiddly work. When he finally finished restoring the model, he put it back up on a high shelf, and there it is, safely out of the way of cats – and mice.

We get Ready for Christmas

IN TWO DAYS' TIME it will be Christmas. The house is full of the spicy smell of the holly and the ivy that decorate the rooms.

For a long while now we have been getting ready. Last month, I went with Mrs Soane to the grocer and tea dealer John Jordan, in High Holborn, just around the corner. Tea, which my Mistress loves to drink with her friends, is so expensive that she buys it herself, just a small amount at a time, and puts it straight into a beautiful decorated tea-caddy, which she locks then keeps the key.

Her Christmas shopping list at grocer Jordan's was a long one. With a wide basket on top of his head, the grocer's boy delivered to the kitchen door bags of currants, raisins and candied peel, as well as spices – nutmegs, mace, cloves and ginger (which makes me sneeze) – and quantities of dark brown sugar. Cooky stored them carefully in a cupboard until baking day came. What a performance that was!

'Master is away today,' she announced in the kitchen one morning shortly afterwards, 'and Mrs Soane will just have a biscuit and cheese and an apple at midday, as she likes to do when he is from home. So you and I, Sally-my-girl, can stir up and bake all day.'

The oven was stoked up, and, after the morning chores were done, Cooky and Sally-my-girl arranged all the ingredients on the kitchen table: they smelt wonderful! Mew and I stared through the kitchen window. The spices and the dried fruit were all arrayed, and I thought of the far-off places they came from, places I had never been. Mew knows a ship's cat who's been to India and told him of the scented groves where the spices grow and where you can pick them off the trees and dig the ginger root from the ground.

There were eggs, of course, and butter, as well as flour from the wooden barrel that stood in the corner of the kitchen, fresh chopped apples, and lots of juicy lemons.

Everything was carefully weighed out, and the large china mixing bowls were washed and warmed. Cooky and Sally-my-girl measured and added and stirred and tasted: one batch was for the cakes, which would finally be iced and decorated, the other for mince pies and tarts, which would be enclosed in pastry in fancy shapes.

This mincemeat mixture had some shredded suet and breadcrumbs added to it as well as minced beef. Both mixtures ended up with a flourish of the brandy bottle.

'Whoops,' Sally giggled, 'bit too much in there; me 'and must've slipped.'

'Slip it did,' said Cooky, 'you put nigh on half a pint in it!' But she laughed and took a pull herself at the round black bottle with its strong smelling liquor.

When everything was done, they covered the bowls with dampened tea cloths to let the mixture settle. Cooky plumped herself down into her capacious armchair with her feet up, while Sally took the opportunity to slip outside into next door's 'area'. Here Harry, Mr Tyndale's footman, with whom she had 'an understanding', was hanging about, pretending to polish his master's boots – which he had already polished more than once that day.

Mew and I looked at each other, the same thought in both our minds: we slipped inside past the snoring figure

of Cooky and into the back kitchen where the bowls
stood on the wooden table. Lifting a corner of one of the
cloths, we sniffed the heavenly perfume of the spices and
the brandy. Mew dipped his paw in to taste. I had a little
taste as well, but it wasn't half as good as it smelt.

Mew, being more adventurous than I, will eat anything
at all. Now one lick led to another: 'Mmmm – it tastes
better as you get used to it,' he said. But after a little while
he went a very funny colour underneath his stripes, and
I said we'd better be off in case he was going to be sick.
So we jumped down from the table and cleared off, but
I'm afraid we left a trail of our paw marks as we went.

When the cakes and pies were baked, they were put
into the larder until Christmas Day.

As the twenty-fifth of December drew near, Master's clients in the country sent him gifts: two hares, one turkey, three plump chickens, and from Matthew's mother in Norfolk came a snow-white goose that she had reared herself.

The turkey was interesting to look at: it had a curved beak and shiny stiff feathers. Will, the footman, plucked it outside in the 'area' on Cook's instructions 'not to get feathers in my kitchen'. He sat on a stool to do it, gripping the bird firmly and working with both hands. Mew and I enjoyed playing with the feathers, and Will saved the largest and strongest to make into quill pens. When it was plucked, the turkey was hung in the cold cupboard called the meat safe until it was time to roast it.

The stuffing was to be made separately, and that involved Cooky herself going to Covent Garden Market with Sally to buy the ingredients. There were to be two sorts of stuffing: sage and onion in one half of the bird and chestnut and bacon in the other. These were 'bound' with beaten eggs, breadcrumbs, and – you guessed it – a good slosh from the brandy bottle. Mew and I could not believe how much stuffing could be crammed into one bird! Sally and Cooky shoved the savoury mixtures in by the fistful at either end until the turkey was full up.

Christmas Day at Number 13

WHEN CHRISTMAS MORNING finally came, everyone in the house was up early. Indeed, it was still dark and quite foggy outside when Mrs Soane and I slipped into Master's bedroom to wish him 'Merry Christmas!'

Later in the morning she went to church and, after a hasty bite to eat at midday, she and I, with Sally, walked out across High Holborn and up Red Lion Street and along Lamb's Conduit Street to the Foundling Hospital in Coram's Fields. The fog had more or less lifted by now, and a pale sun shone, but it was still cold enough for Mrs Soane to wear her muff to keep her hands warm, and her fur tippet, as well as her bonnet.

We often visit the Foundling Hospital. It is for children who have been 'found', who have no families, or whose families are too poor to bring them up at home. They are taken to live and go to school here, the boys in one half of the building and the girls in the other. Sally had been a 'foundling', and Mrs Soane had made friends with her when Sally was just a little girl at the Hospital. When Sally turned fifteen, about six years ago (she doesn't know her exact age), she had come to work for the Soanes and live as part of the family.

I like going there because I play with the children, and on this occasion I was especially welcomed by them because Mrs Soane had made some pretty coloured purses full of sixpences – one coin each for the children as a Christmas present. She had taught me to carry these purses in my teeth and drop them into the children's outstretched hands for the six pences to be shared out. Today there were quite a few visitors, and all the children were dressed in their best for Christmas and were rushing about the place in excitement.

We didn't stay for long because the dinner had to be supervised at home; it was to be served, as usual, between four and five o'clock in the afternoon, so the turkey had to roast for hours in order to be ready in time, and the table to be beautifully laid for the feast.

It was growing dark when we turned into our square, and the lamplighter was already lighting the lamps. It always seemed so quiet in the house without the pupils there. I thought about my friend Matthew and hoped he had got home safely on the coach, with the splendid cake Cook had baked as a present for his family. Mrs Soane had made little bonnets and mufflers for his sisters and sent a big bundle of more of John and George's outgrown clothes for him and his brothers. I hoped they were having a merry Christmas all together.

Now my Mistress put on her evening gown, with a matching green silk turban with a long feather fastened in place with a pearl brooch. She wore her finest green slippers, made of a soft leather called kid, and down she went to the drawing-room.

The yellow drawing-room is somewhere I tend to avoid, because I am afraid of putting a paw wrong in that elegant room. The yellow silk of the curtains and the sofa is so delicate, and the paint so bright and shiny, and besides there are spindly fire screens and torchères and all sorts of precious things on the tables. When it was first being decorated, I went in to have a little peep. I got yellow paint on my fur from brushing against the wall and had to have that bit of fur cut off, which I didn't enjoy much! So I always steer clear of the drawing-room after that.

Tonight, though, I trotted in decorously following my mistress (and keeping to the middle of the room in case someone had taken it into their head to paint the walls again). We made for the fire, which was so bright and welcoming. The candles in the beautiful glass chandelier sparkled, and the arrangements of glossy holly and ivy looked soft and dark against the brightly coloured walls.

All of a sudden Master picked me up and took me outside the drawing-room. He was behaving quite mysteriously. He said he had a secret that he wanted to let me in on. He opened a small box, covered in black velvet, and slipped what was glittering inside it round my neck, wrapping it round twice. It was his present to Mrs Soane – a diamond necklace! Then he picked me up and carried me back into the drawing-room and pushed me gently toward her. She gasped when she saw my new 'collar'. I jumped on to her lap so that she could unclasp it, and she put it on and twirled about in front of the mirror over the fireplace, looking at it from every angle.

*Fanny helps Mr and Mrs Soane and their guests exchange
Christmas gifts in the yellow drawing-room.*

'Oh, look how it sparkles!' She was quite overcome by the beauty of it, and it did look lovely round her slim neck.

She gave Master a beautiful volume of his architectural drawings, which she had had specially bound into a handsome book, as well as some gloves she had knitted to keep him warm on his travels to building sites. For me she had made a pillow stuffed with the softest goose feathers, with my initial embroidered on it: *E*, in scarlet silk stitches!

Then it was time to go downstairs to the Christmas feast. The smell of roast turkey rose up from the kitchen into the dining-room; here the table was laid for twelve people as friends were coming in.

The turkey was as delicious as it smelt; the stuffing went down a treat, and every bit was eaten. The mince pies were rich and the pastry feather light. After dinner toasts were drunk to 'Absent friends!' and 'Good luck in the New Year!'

I slipped next door to chat to Mew.

For his Christmas present he'd been given a delicious fish pie, in the shape of a fish, with fish scales made of pastry. I helped him lick out the dish.

That night I slept very soundly on my new pillow.

Amewsing Ourselves
in the Catacombs

After Christmas, not until Twelfth Night, which is the sixth of January, did Mew and I have our own party, when we thought it would be 'a*mew*sing' to go down to the *cat*acombs right at the bottom of the house.

I have told you how Master likes shadows and mysterious light and half-light. Well, we decided to have our own shadow-play, as he does when he shows visitors around the mysterious spaces he has created, lit only by moonlight shining in from a low window, or sometimes by two little oil lamps in niches, as used in ancient times. Mew and I love it down here, making shadows dance on the walls and floor. Mew is very good at shadow-play – being a bit of a show-off as you will have understood by now. He makes his tail into a snake and *hiss-s-s-es* as it wriggles along the wall; his paws become spiders dangling above my head. We were laughing so much that we collapsed in front of the little coal fire, and before we knew it, we'd fallen fast asleep. Gradually the lamps ran out of oil and the fire, too, died down to a rosy glow.

We awoke, stiff and cold, in darkness complete except for the thin moonlight playing on the antique stone faces, which glimmered weirdly. They looked spookier than we had ever seen them before.

The door had been shut – the servants thinking we were upstairs and my Mistress that we were down in the kitchen. We couldn't get out! We were alone with these mysterious beings in their silent underworld – or were we?

'Help!' whispered Mew. 'What was that noise?'

'Nothing, there was no noise,' I said lightly, while flattening myself against the wall, just in case.

'I'm sure I heard something moving,' said Mew, 'what if – what if one of these old creatures comes alive and tries to EAT US?'

'Mew,' I said, 'creatures as old as these have been dead for so long they're hardly going to come alive now! Besides, they don't need to eat,' I added, 'I mean, they wouldn't be interested in eating us even if they did, which they don't...' I paused. There was something moving stealthily towards us in the darkness: a large creature, whose shadow on the wall had huge whiskers and ears the size of black bats. Scarcely daring to breathe, Mew and I clung silently to one another as the creature came nearer and nearer until we made out two glinting eyes in the darkness and heard it sniffing: it was a rat.

He was as surprised to see us as we were to see him. We said nothing; he said nothing. We and the rats ignore one another: they go their way, we go ours. We're too big for them, they're too tough for us.

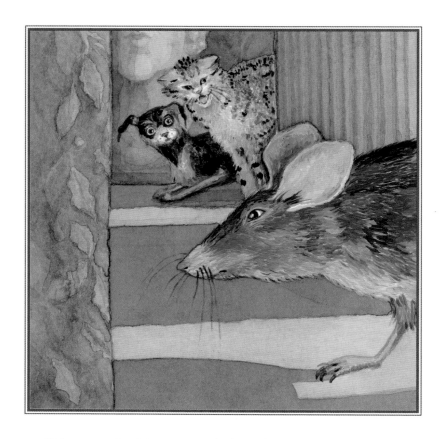

We've worked it out, and that's how it is round here. (Mice are one thing, rats another.) We stayed where we were; silently he went on his way.

Mew and I breathed again. Then he said, '*We* can get out the way *he* got in. C'mon!' He set off, following the rat's trail, sniffing carefully at the ground so as not to lose it. Luckily cat eyesight is acute in the dark.

In a far corner at the back of the room a dip in the stone floor made a hole we could crawl through into the passage. Years of rats coming and going had increased the size of the gap enough for Mew and me to squeeze underneath. It wasn't easy, but we just made it, pushing and pulling to help each other through. The passage brought us round to the back entrance of the kitchen. I know how to push up the latch of that door with my paw (Cooky doesn't know I know this) so we could open it easily.

I've never been so glad to see the familiar kitchen, with its big wooden table, brightly gleaming pans, and, especially Cooky's old armchair, with its soft cushions. There we flopped, dusty and cold, to spend the rest of the night, until the early glimmering of dawn when Will came in, yawning and rubbing his eyes, and we both slipped past him unseen and back to our own beds.

1815, an Unhappy Year

So THE WINTER DRAWS ON, the evenings becoming darker and darker. Outside, there is often a fog or misty drizzle, and the lamplighter seems to come earlier and earlier in the afternoon to light the lamps in the Square.

Indoors, however many fires are lit, still the house seems darker, almost as though the mist outside has invaded it, coming through the doors and up the stairs, pervasive, clammy, damp, and dismal.

For the whole of this year Mrs Soane has not been well.
Although she never complains, I know she is often in pain.
She spends a lot of time in bed. Sally is a comforting
presence when Mrs Soane feels bad, and when Sally has
to go out on errands, or help Cook in the kitchen, she tells
my Mistress, 'Fanny'll keep you company now. On guard,
Fanny!' and I curl up next to her on her bed or look out
of the window for Sally or Master returning home.

Master is working harder than ever. He comes to
bed later and later, sitting up sometimes until midnight
over drawings and revisions for buildings – despite
complaining of how his eyes ache. My Mistress and
I hear him coming upstairs, however quietly he treads
(he always takes off his shoes so as not to disturb us)
and see the glow of his candle as he turns into his
room, next door to hers.

Today is indeed a sad one, the saddest of my life. I know the date exactly and I shall always remember it.

Wednesday, the twenty-second of November 1815

It began as usual: Sally and I walked in the Square, although she was so anxious to get back to our Mistress that we fairly ran round the gardens and then straight back into the house, so that she could go and look after her. The doctor came to visit. When he had left, shaking his head and talking in a low voice to Master, I sat outside her – our – bedroom so I could hear if she called out for me.

The house was very quiet: the maids took care not to clatter their pails as they washed the floors, and Will opened the front door noiselessly to friends who came to ask how my Mistress was. I saw my chance, after Sally left the door to the bedroom ajar, to slip softly inside. I jumped on to the bed as lightly as I could. She lay with her eyes closed, but when she felt my arrival on the bed, she opened them and smiled at me; she stroked my head, as she had done so often and often before.

'Fanny, my dear,' she whispered, her voice was weak, but still held all her kindness and gentleness, 'Fan, whatever becomes of me, you will look after Master, won't you?

And be a loving companion to him, as you have always been to me? For,' her voice sank so low that I could only just make out what she was saying, 'if anything happens to me he will be very lonely and...'

She stopped, her voice choked with the tears that she tried without success to stop from rolling down her pale cheeks. Gently, I licked them away, then snuggled down next to her on the bed, so that she would know I understood.

Sally came in to give her some medicine the doctor had prescribed to ease her pain and some water to sip; she put her arm round our Mistress to make it easier for her to drink. Master came in and sat with her for a bit, and Sally carried me out on to the landing. She and I huddled together at the head of the stairs, me on her lap and she holding me close to her for comfort. Slowly the morning wore on. Occasionally Sally got up and we peeped into the bedroom to see if my Mistress needed anything, but, alas, there was nothing she could need any more – for at twenty minutes past one o'clock in the middle of the day, she died.

Thursday, the thirtieth of November

The last few days have passed in a blur, and now it is the evening before my Mistress is to be buried. Although the house is quieter than usual, there seems a busy feeling about it, as visitors come to talk to Master and say good-bye to my Mistress: 'to pay their respects', as they call it.

She has been brought downstairs to the library to lie in her coffin. It is covered in a shiny black velvet cloth, and on each corner are black plumes. The window shutters are closed, even in the daytime, and candles glow softly

in the gloom. The air is chill, no fire is lit there; I feel as
if the fire and warmth have gone from the house too.

Sometimes I creep up to see Matthew in the Drawing
Office; sometimes I go down to the kitchen with Sally,
but mostly I curl up in my Mistress's wardrobe, on the soft
slippers she loved, beneath her dresses and her favourite
shawl of fine green wool. The scent of lavender and rose

petals lingers there. I would rather sleep here than in my
bed in 'our' bedroom. Sally seems to understand, and we
have taken my bed out on to the landing for the moment.

Tomorrow is her funeral and tonight, all night, two
of the menservants and two of the pupils will take it in
turns to sit by her coffin in the library. Mew and I will
keep them company.

Friday, the first of December

I don't think any of us slept much last night. This morning all the household, and the pupils too, were dressed in black. Sally even put a black collar on me, which she had made from some scraps left over from sewing her mourning apron.

The coaches drew up outside Number 13 to take Mrs Soane's coffin and the mourners to her funeral. The horses drawing them had black ostrich feathers on their bridles; the coachmen had black bands on their hats and wore grey gloves. Mr Tyndale, Mew's

Master, and his family – all dressed in black – climbed into their carriage. Then it was Master's turn to get into the waiting carriage. Carefully choosing my moment, I jumped into the coach after him, and sat motionless under the seat opposite him; he was too distraught to notice that I was there. I was determined to come and say good-bye to my beloved Mistress for the last time.

Slowly the horses clip-clopped out of the Square and started on the familiar route I had walked so often with my Mistress, across High Holborn up Lamb's Conduit Street, then northwards, up Gray's Inn Lane and finally to the burial ground at St Pancras.

The servants and the pupils had walked on ahead.
I waited outside in the churchyard during the funeral
service, and then stood with everyone at the graveside as
her coffin was brought out of the chapel and lowered in.
Earth rattled down on her coffin lid; the spades of the
grave-diggers swiftly threw in more and more until her
grave was full. Master turned away then, and he and
I walked slowly, side by side, to the waiting coach.

Christmas 1815 and New Year 1816: I remember my promise to my Mistress

JUST A FEW SHORT WEEKS have passed, and how different everything is now at home without my Mistress.

For a while I have continued to sleep in her wardrobe, to remind myself of her, feeling that she was somehow still here, that she would come into the room, throw off her shawl and bonnet, and lie on the bed to rest after one of our walks, as she had used to do.

Gradually Master has gone back to his work. His pupils are extra obedient so as not to upset him, but they don't always get things right, of course, and then I'm afraid he raises his voice and shouts at them, telling them that they must do their work all over again and they're wasting precious paper. I've taken to barking when he does that, in a sort of chorus with him, which makes him smile and the boys laugh, and the sound of their laughter cheers him up again.

Just lately Sally moved my bed into Master's bedroom. I have begun to sleep there, and sometimes I even creep under his bedcover where Sally puts the warming pan in for him.

May 1816: the Beautiful Tomb

I<small>T'S VERY EXCITING</small>; Master is building a tomb for my Mistress: a large one, with pillars and a domed cover. I told Mew all about it, and how it will stand prominently in the churchyard where she's buried. In the Drawing Office I showed him the sketch one of the boys had done of it, under Matthew's supervision.

Now the beautiful tomb is built, and Master and I often walk together to visit it. He orders the carriage to take us back home, 'on account of your short legs, Fanny,' he says, but I know that he gets a bit more tired these days as well.

Matthew has grown very tall and even paler if that is possible, and Master depends on him and likes talking to him as he was such a favourite of Mrs Soane. They go together to the buildings he is designing, but I don't go with them because they walk so much faster on their two legs than I do on my four short ones. But I wait for Master's return, and we often eat dinner together – me with my bowl by the fire, he at table – in companionable silence, most often, but he also talks about where he's been and what he's been doing, as he used to talk to her.

I have remembered my promise to my Mistress.

Fanny keeps Mr Soane company in the library.

Editor's Epilogue

Fanny lived comfortably and quietly with her Master, cherished and loved always as one of his household and on account of her many years spent with his dear wife.

It is not recorded what became of Mew, but I expect they enjoyed some more happy times together frisking about the house and the square.

When Fanny died at Number 13 on Christmas Day, 1820, she was about seventeen years old – a great age! Soane wrote in his diary: 'My dear little Fanny died this evening at 12 o'clock – faithful animal, farewell'. Two days later he recorded: 'Fanny buried in a lead coffin in the morning at 7 o'clock... Alas poor Fanny! Faithful, affectionate, disinterested friend, long, very long will thou live in my recollection – Farewell!'

In order to make sure that she did live on in his memory, and, incidentally ensuring that we are reminded of her to this day, Soane transferred the little lead coffin containing her remains to the tall stone tomb he had designed for her, which you can see in the Monk's Yard, in the basement of the house.

On it he had inscribed:

ALAS, POOR FANNY!

Soane, who was knighted and became Sir John Soane, died in 1837 at the grand old age of eighty-four. He was well and healthy right up until shortly before his death, and he died peacefully, at home in the magical house he had spent so many years creating. He is buried at St Pancras, next to his wife and eldest son.

Today, if you stand on the front doorstep of Number 13, you look out upon the Square of Lincoln's Inn Fields, which is still much as Fanny saw and enjoyed it when she lived here. There aren't the same sorts of people going about their daily round, like the lamplighter or the milkmaid delivering milk, and there are fewer family houses and more offices. But the gardens are still there, where Fanny walked every day, and although there are, of course, several modern buildings, for London is a city which is always changing, still there is much, too, that she would recognise. And if you turn and look back into the house, apart from the electric light, everything is kept as Sir John Soane had it – there are even the same crowds of visitors still!

And is that...? Could it be...? A little black wavy tail disappearing round the corner of the dining-room and the skittering of four small paws up the stairs to the pupils' Drawing Office?

In the breakfast room at the Museum, you can see this portrait of Fanny, painted by James Ward in 1822, after her death.

We would like to thank the following individuals who have generously subscribed to *The Journal of Mrs Soane's Dog, Fanny.* Many have chosen a personal dedication which we are happy to record.

DEIDRE HOPKINS
for Ben, Lizzie, Anna,
Florence & Lucca

OSCAR LEWISOHN
To Fanny from four-legged
Millie Lewisohn and her
two-legged friends: Jenny,
Sophie, Max, Oscar, Dominic,
Louisa, Joe, Amy, Sam,
Lottie, Ben & Alexander

GEORGE LAURENCE
for Tom, Cathy, Ben, Claire,
Eddie, Lulu, Teddy & Jessica

CHRISTIAN LEVETT
for Chappy &
Charlie-Bear Levett

LULU LYTLE
for Tom, Bunny & Xan

CHAS MILLER
& BIRCH COFFEY
In memory of Lizzie

HUGH MONK
for Grace, Harry & Theo

AMICIA OLDFIELD
for Edward Oldfield,
Ajax, Alceste, Arthur
& Rose de Moubray

JANINE RENSCH
for Elise & Jessica Rensch

IAN AND WENDY
SAMPSON
for our grandchildren, Meghan,
George, David & Ranulph

THE MARQUESS
& MARCHIONESS
OF SALISBURY
for Miss Iris Cecil, Miss Matilda
Cecil, Master Thomas Cecil,
Miss Martha Campbell &
Master Patrick Campbell

CYNDY & JOHN
SPURDLE
for Maud & Nick with
puppy love from Georgie;
for Isabel, Hadley & Will
with love from lucky Labs
Coal and Skye

CORAL SAMUEL
Tom's Fennel, Peter's Kola
and all *the dogs*

SUSIE THOMSON
for Jamie Elwes

KATHLEEN ELIZABETH
SPRINGHORN
for Lillie and in memory
of beloved Westie Harry
(1986-2002)

BILL & SUSIE TYNE
for Oscar

NICHOLAS & LAVINIA
WALLOP
for Eve, Alexander,
Edward, Felix, Dickon
and Cecilia

Published 2010 by Sir John Soane's Museum
Registered Charity Number 313609
www.soane.org

ISBN 978-0-9558762-3-3

This book would not have been possible without the generous help and
advice of Susan Palmer, the Archivist of Sir John Soane's Museum and
author of *The Soanes at Home*.

We would also like to thank Mike Nicholson, the Museum's
Development Director, for his support and encouragement.
Also, the Cecil cat, Gabriel, the model for Mew.

Produced by Brubaker & Ford Ltd www.brubakerford.com
Designed by Amelia Edwards and Daniel Devlin

Computer graphics by Daniel Devlin, including combining the Soane
Museum's original watercolours with Francesca Martin's new illustrations

Edited by Roberta Butler
For Sir John Soane's Museum, edited by Susan Palmer

Printed and bound in Singapore by Imago

THE 3 IN 1 RIDDLES BOOK FOR SMART KIDS AGE 9-12

Difficult Riddles and Brain Teasers for Kids and The Whole Family

1st Edition

Smart Kids Publishing

Table of Contents

Riddles have been around for millennia. The history of recorded riddles stretches back to the discovery of the Rhind Mathematical papyrus. Puzzling over brain teasers and conundrums was the meme and viral messaging of yesteryear.

People encounter riddles continuously on social media feeds and the puzzle pages at the back of newspapers and magazines. However, we almost never recognize them as riddles. This is because riddles have integrated so well into the fabric of our society.

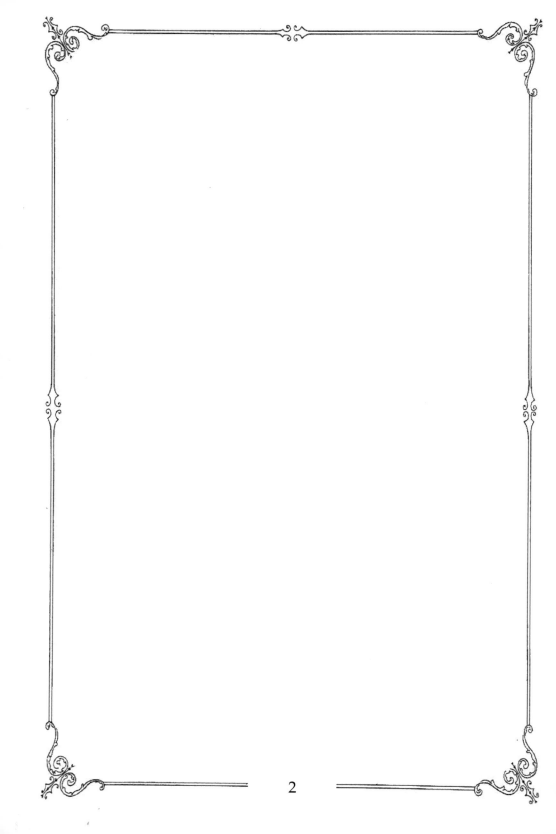

The History of Riddles

Where did the asking and answering of riddles come from? It's not hard to find the oldest riddles on the internet, and they are still able to get us scratching our heads. This is proof that accessibility and age are no hindrance when it comes to being a tough nut to crack. With only the briefest dive into the distant past, it is possible for us to reach in and grasp a riddle as old as time:

Why did the little feathered chicken cross over the road? – you may remember this riddle from your childhood. The answer to this puzzling question changes with the age of the audience. It's "it wants to cross over to the other side" in childhood. When you reach adulthood, the answer can become one of many:

"Give me about five minutes alone with that big mouth chicken,
and I'll find out"
- The Mafia

"What on earth was this bird walking around all over the countryside for?
- Jerry Seinfeld

"I missed one?"
- Colonel Sanders

This is not the oldest riddle, but it gives us a good idea about how riddles managed to become well-known before the rise of global connectivity.

Oedipus and the Sphinx

Oedipus, a famous mythological hero of Ancient Greece, was better known for his riddle-answering capabilities before his name became associated with Freud's. Oedipus's adventure with the Sphinx has survived and thrived in modern times. Just read J.K. Rowling's fourth book in the Harry Potter series, and you will easily recognize the riddle-posing Sphinx character. In fact, J.K. Rowling inserts riddles into many parts of her wizarding book series.

The story goes that Oedipus went to the city of Thebes and found the city in mourning because a monstrous creature had eaten their king. The creature is described as having the face of a beautiful woman, but with the body of a lioness, and the wings of a mountain eagle – a Sphinx.

The Sphinx had blocked one of the gates to the city and demanded of anyone who wanted to enter or exit through the gates to answer her riddle. When they got the answer wrong, the Sphinx would devour the unlucky traveler. The legend goes that the Muses, who were goddesses of the arts, had given the Sphinx the riddle as a gift.

Thebes Problem Riddle was this:

> *"What has 4 legs in the morning time,*
> *2 legs when it's noon,*
> *and 3 legs when evening comes around?*
> *Tell me, tell me, tell me soon."*

The brainiest inhabitants of Thebes had all died trying to answer the riddle, and as no one had ever returned to the city, no one knew what the riddle was in advance. The throne of Thebes and the princess's hand in marriage had been offered as a reward, so Oedipus decided to give answering it a try.

When Oedipus reached the city gate, the Sphinx was waiting there in the midst of the dusty road. She asked him the question as he approached and halted so he was forward facing her enormous paws.

Oedipus answered the Sphinx: "Man. Man is born and crawls around on all four limbs as a baby, then walks on two legs in the prime of life. Finally, he uses a stick to help him hobble around in old age." This was the correct answer. In a rage, the Sphinx flew off and was never seen by anyone ever again. Oedipus went on to become Oedipus Rex, King of Thebes.

A Greek poet called Homer wrote (or recorded) this story in around 9th or 8th century BCE.

Samson and the Lion (550 BCE)

Samson was a very strong protagonist in the Old Testament Bible. In the Judges Book of the Bible, Samson was able to kill a lion with his bare hands. Similar imagery was used to demonstrate the strength of Hercules in Greek mythology.

Samson visits the lion bones later and discovers the lion's body is being used by bees to build a large hive. He takes some of the honey and eats it and gives some to his parents to eat as well. This is symbolic of many things, but Samson also uses this memory as the basis for the riddle he poses to guests at one of his feasts.

> *"Something to consume out of a voracious eater.*
> *Out of the strong comes something sweet.*
> *What am I?"*

The answer is actually an open-ended question. And the feast guests got it correct because they cheated by asking Samson's wife for the solution to the puzzle.

> *"What is sweeter than honey, you may ask?*
> *What can be stronger than a lion?"*

It is more of a deduction than an answer. In Bible times, honey was the sweetest thing and lions were the strongest eaters known to humans. You could call this answer more of an extrapolation, then a solution.

Mathematical Papyrus
to around 1650 BCE)

The ancient Rhind papyrus problem is translated as follows:

> 7 Houses = (blank)
> 49 cats = 2,801
> 343 mice = 5,602
> 2,301 spelt = 11,204
> (blank) hekat = 16,807
> Total 19,607 = total 19,607

The papyrus was translated as a multiplication algorithm: $7 - 7^2 - 7^3 - 7^4 - 7^5$ is the left column. 1 x 2,801 all the way up to 7 x 2,801 is the right column. Both give the same total with two different ways of getting there. Have you spotted the mistake? The correct answer on the other side of 11,204 spelt should be 2,401, not 2,301.

Someone in the late 18th century managed to turn the Rhind papyrus algorithm into a famous riddle we still have fun asking today:

> *There are 7 houses.*
> *And in every house, there are 7 cats.*
> *And each cat snatches 7 mice.*
> *Every mouse ate 7 seeds.*
>
> *That stopped 7 tons of wheat growing.*
> *How much is that altogether?*

The Rhind papyrus may have also been the source for the St. Ives Riddle:

"As I went to St. Ives,
on the road, I met 9 goodwives,
and every goodwife had 9 bags,
and every bag had 9 big cats,
and every big cat had 9 little kittens.
How many were going to St. Ives?"

The answer is mainly agreed to be 1. The kittens, cats, bags, and wives were all going in the opposite direction.

Can you imagine the excitement and discussion around the firesides in Europe in the evenings when the father returned from town many miles away and asked his family this riddle? That is why riddles are as popular today as they have been for thousands of years.

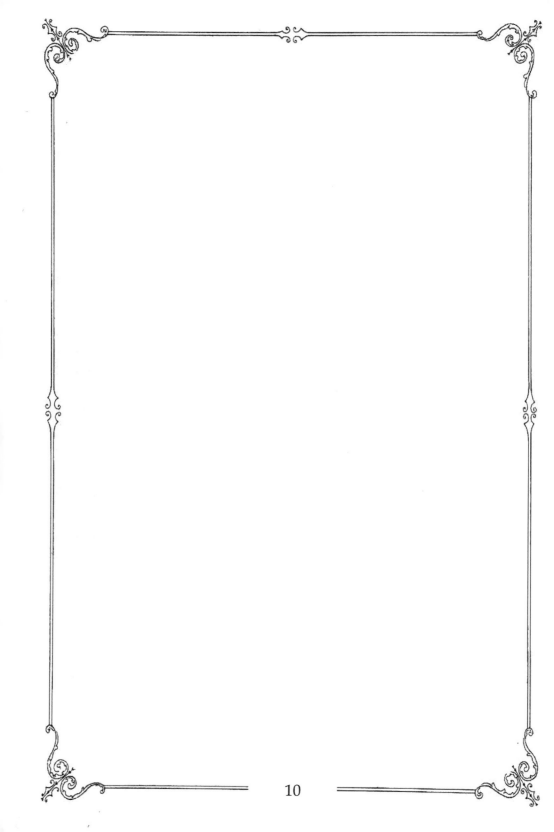

How Riddles
Sharpen the Adult Mind

By regularly solving puzzles and riddles, the adult brain is forced to build connections between brain cells. This is a very important physiological benefit for the brain to continue doing as the neurons' age. When these connections are nurtured, your thought processes and mental speed accelerate and focus.

A little-known fact: Jigsaw puzzles, riddles, and painting are especially good for improving the short-term memory of people over the age of 25 years. It section of the brain that deals with short-term memory are stimulated by these activities as they help us to remember colors and shapes. We visualize the bigger picture, which helps the brain figure out how it all fits together.

Puzzles and riddles imbue us with the confidence to give answering a problem a try. This might be done through a long-winded procedure of trial and a fair bit of error, but we have a feeling of accomplishment when we finally get it right. We must look at a situation in a different way when confronted with a riddle. If the riddle is spoken out loud or written down on paper, the visual-spatial reasoning part of the brain is stimulated in both cases.

No feeling quite matched the feeling of solving a riddle. The triumph of getting to the bottom of a mysterious puzzle is a real mood booster. When your mood is elevated by using your brain, the risk of dementia or Alzheimer's is considerably lowered. Using your brain causes new brain cell neurons to reconnect.

These are just some of the positive effects of adults setting out to solve riddles whenever they have the time to sit and think (or even sit and laugh).

How Riddles
Help Develop a Child's Brain

It's very important to help children learn outside of digital networks. Far the best way of doing this is by sharing riddles and puzzles together: they are of huge benefit in improving a child's mental state and lifting their mood.

Riddles help introduce children to a more intellectual way of having a laugh. There's nothing to beat the happiness and laughter in a child's face when they hear the answer to a funny riddle.

The skills learnt when asking and answering riddles have a long-term benefit for critical thinking and problem solving. These are talents that are extremely valuable in the workforce.

Riddles encourage reading and calculation. If you start a child off with riddles when they are old enough to understand the premise, the child or children will have a decided advantage when they reach school age. Additionally, the lucky children who have a family who shares telling each other riddles are found to have developed a deeper comprehension of many subjects.

Riddles expand a child's vocabulary and social skills. They gain the ability to share riddles and the answers to the riddles with others. Children definitely need a good grasp of the concept, reasoning, and wording behind the riddle, so they can then attempt to solve it first before passing it on to others.

Finally, nothing bonds a family together more – especially during long car trips, sitting in waiting rooms, and keeping busy minds active – than asking, puzzling over, and solving a riddle!

Part 1
Riddles for Kids from 9-10

"What Am I?"
Riddles for Kids

Asking children "What am I?" riddles is a great way to introduce them to the whole concept of riddling. The best place to start a riddling family tradition is in the car. Asking and answering riddles isn't the only thing you can do during a long and boring journey, however.

As a family, you can also come up with entirely new riddles that have never been thought of before. This not only brings the family closer together and makes the time pass enjoyably, but the children will also get to impress their friends by asking them to solve unique riddles at a later date.

The best way to ask and answer riddles if there are very young children is to pair up into teams. An older sibling with a young one or a mother paired up with a younger child. In this way, the very young child doesn't feel left out of the game and gets to share in the triumph when their team gets and answer correct.

The best system for car riddling is for each team to take turns asking a riddle out loud and secretly knowing the answer. Much laughter and giggling will ensue as the other team muses suggested answers out loud. The riddle-asking team can spice things up by saying "hot", "warmer", or "cold" if the answer is close to a proper solution or miles off target.

Best "What am I?"
Riddles for Family Car Journeys

1. 3 eyes have I
   All of them in a column
   When my 1 red eye opens
   All freeze and stop
   What am I?

2. No sooner am I spoken out loud,
   then immediately I am broken.
   What am I?

3. I fall, but I never break.
   What am I?
   I break, but I never fall.
   What am I?

4. My outside is discarded,
   and then my inside is cooked.
   My outside is eaten,
   and then my inside is discarded.
   What am I?

5. I never was,
   but somehow, I will always be.
   Nobody has ever seen me,
   nor will they ever see me.

   I am trusted by everyone
   who lives here on planet earth.
   What am I?

6. I get wetter the more I dry.
    What am I?

7. I am uttered as 1 letter.
    I am written using 3.
    2 letters there, but
    Only 2 letters are in me.

    I am a double,
    I am single.
    I can be red, blue, black, grey, green, brown.
    You can read me from both ends,

    I read the same either way.
    This riddle can make you frown.
    What am I?

8. I have no weight,
    But you can see me when I'm big.
    When you have me in a bucket,
    I make it lighter.
    I make you work harder,
    To get things done.
    What am I?

9. I am full of holes, yet water I hold.
    What am I?

10. What thing runs, and never walks.
    It has a mouth and never talks.
    It has one head however, it doesn't weep
    It also has a bed, but somehow it never even sleeps
    What am I?

11. I fly when the wind blows,
    yet I don't ever manage to go anywhere.
    What am I?

12. I start with this letter from the alphabet "P".
    I end with the letter "E".
    I have lots of letters on me.
    What am I?

13. I come out at nighttime even though I'm not called.
    Then I magically disappear during the daytime.
    Even though I'm still there,
    you can't see me because of something else.
    What am I?

14. When I'm young, I'm tall.
    When I'm short, I'm old.
    What am I?

15. My name begins with this letter
    from the alphabet, "E" but
    I only have one letter.
    What am I?

16. I'm very easy for you to get into,
    but somehow, I'm sadly very difficult to get out of.
    What am I?

17. I was bought for meals, yet I am never eaten.
    What am I?

18. I travel around the world,
    yet I always stay in one spot.
    What am I?

19. *I have 72 ponytails, one thousand feet,*
    and 20 Hello Kitty handbags.
    What am I?

20. *I am planted in a farmer's field,*
    and yet I never grow.
    What am I?

Best Trick Questions for Children

There are two recognized categories of riddles: conundrums and enigmas, but it isn't important for kids to know this as it is for them to recognize other differences. Teach children the difference between rhyme and a riddle. A riddle might rhyme, but it always needs an answer. A rhyme or nursery rhyme is a song or poem about nonsense situations.

You don't need to classify a riddle as one of two types, however. As long as your riddle requires some thought to figure out, and ultimately has an answer or solution, it's good. Trick questions fall into this category. Asking tricky questions and brain teasers is a great way to take a child's mind off something and get them to focus on the riddle at hand.

Never let a child sit and work something out on their own. It's essential that this is a fun, interactive game to do altogether.

1. *What goes up,*
    When the rain comes down?

2. *What is only black and white,*
    But is it also red?

3. *An aero plane crashes down exactly*
    exactly between the two countries.
    Where are the survivors buried?

4. *I have three apples in my hand.*
    Then you take two of the apples away from me.
    How many apples do you have?

5. I am looking out the car window,
    and in my view is an electric train chuffing
    along the train tracks that run from
    North to South.
    What direction is the smoke going?

6. If some months have 31 days,
    and some months have 30 days.
    Then how many months of the year have 28 days?

7. What weighs more?
    A pound of feather down or a pound of lead?

8. To what question can
    you NEVER reply "Yes" to,
    truthfully?

9. What can you put into a barrel of water,
    so that it weighs less?

10. The more this thing spreads,
    the less you are able to see it.

When younger children have gotten the hang of how the trick question concept works, you can expand riddling games to include brain teasers and questions that will challenge their logic, powers of deduction, and patience!

Best Brain Teasers
for Children

1. What is absolutely the biggest arch in the world?

2. What will never get wetter outside,
   even when it rains and pours?

3. What has a head, and also a tail,
   but doesn't have a body?

4. What can you easily catch,
   but it was never thrown?

5. What goes up and down and all around,
   but somehow always remains in the same place?

6. What is possible to break,
   but is never dropped, bent, or held?

7. What can you have,
   and when you have this thing,
   you would like to share it with me?
   But when you do share it,
   whether you mean to or not,
   suddenly you don't have this thing anymore?

8. What is the first thing everyone does when
   they wake up in the morning?

9. What letter is it from the alphabet which
   means you can drink it and
   serve to guests when they visit?

10. *Freddy's father has 4 sons:*
    three of the sons are named
    One, Two, and – you've guessed it – Three!
    Take a guess as to the name of son number four?

Part 2
Riddles for Kids from 10-12

Best Riddles for Children
that Will Help Develop Logical Thinking

Riddles have always had a dual purpose: to entertain and to boost thinking skills. This is especially important in the development of logical thinking in young children. By stimulating young minds, you engage the developing vital parts of the brain. It sharpens deductive skills and helps boosts cognitive reasoning.

There are many positive benefits from asking answering riddles besides wiling away long hours and staving off boredom. Riddling encourages bonding and strengthens relationships within the individual family units. Asking riddles can also help children overcome social awkwardness because they interact with other people as they pass the riddle along.

Riddles can teach children new words and mental images as they try and puzzle out what it means. This expands on vocabulary and comprehension.

1. *What letter of the alphabet contains water?*

2. *Can you take a guess as to what you will find at the end of the rainbow?*

3. *A red path leads to a red little cottage.*
   Inside the cottage is a red floor.
   On the floor are a red table and a red chair.
   Next to the chair is a red window.
   Next to the window is a red door.
   What color is the staircase?

4. What has two hands and a face,
   but doesn't have arms or legs?

5. What ends in "E", starts with "E",
   and yet somehow magically only has one letter?

6. Why cannot someone who's living in
   The city of London be buried in New York?

7. What is better to be broken before you use it?

8. Where does Friday come before Thursday?

9. How on earth is this even possible?
   I throw the ball as hard as I can and it
   returns to me without anyone or
   is anything touching it?

10. What has a beautiful, long neck,
    but doesn't have a head?

11. What did one sea say out loud to the other sea?

12. The man fell off a very tall ladder but
    did not hurt himself. Why?

13. What is always used by other people,
    but definitely belongs to you?

14. What goes up, and never comes down?

15. What do you always answer,
    yet a question hasn't been asked?

16. *Think about this.*
    You are in a boat in the midst of the seas and
    your boat springs a leak, however,
    you are also surrounded by hungry sharks.
    What to do?

17. *What key can't open a door?*

18. *What key can't open a door?*

19. *If I give you one dollar,*
    what is the easiest way to double it?

20. *What does every person have,*
    and is also impossible to lose?

21. *This word is actually spelled incorrectly in*
    every English dictionary.
    What word is this?

22. *What little tree found everywhere in the world can*
    be carried in your hand.

23. *Can you go without sleeping for 5 days?*

24. *What is completely filled with keys,*
    yet none of them are used to open a door?

25. *What has a big horn,*
    and yet can't make a noise with it?

26. *What is as large as an elephant,*
    yet weighs nothing at all?

27. Who keeps their shoes on even
    when they are sleeping?

28. What can still teach you after being turned on its
    back and opened up?

29. When you have a problem,
    who can you count on?

30. What is actually right there in your face and
    yet you cannot see it?

31. Where are streets, shops,
    and whole towns,
    but no people are there?

32. What is black, white, and blue?

33. Mr. Red lives in the Red House.
    Mrs. Black resides in a black House.
    Mr. Green lives in the Green House.
    Who lives in the White House?

34. How far is it possible for you to run into
    the forest or woods?

35. What happens one time in your lifetime,
    and then twice in minus a minute.
    Yet it doesn't happen in one hundred years?

36. This is an odd number.
    If you take one letter away,
    it becomes even.
    What number is it?

37. *What has two hands but can never clap?*

38. *If a yellow residence is made with yellow bricks and stuff, and a brown house is made with brown bricks and stuff, then what is a greenhouse made with?*

39. *If you throw a white pebble right into the Red Sea, what then happens?*

40. *If you throw a black pebble into the Red Sea, what happens?*

41. *What has 4 legs but somehow still can't walk?*

42. *If 2 is a good company, and 3 is a crowd, what are 4 and 5?*

43. *If a squirrel, a chipmunk, and a hamster climb up an oak tree at the same time, who will manage to eat the nuts first?*

44. *What word will have 5 letters, yet it becomes shorter when you add 2 letters to the thing?*

45. *My pockets are definitely empty yet I still manage to have something in there. What is it?*

46. *What can be served, but never eaten?*

47. *What can you whip and beat, and yet it never cries?*

48. What is brown and green,
    and has 4 eyes,
    but cannot see.

49. This is bought for people to eat,
    and yet it is never eaten?

50. Why does a teddy bear never hungry?

Best "Think Outside of the Box" Riddles for Children

It is our job as parents to take the time in teaching kids how to think outside of the box. This encourages them to be independent, creative thinkers. These skills are an often-neglected part of school curriculums.

By nurturing ingenuity and creativity in our children, it naturally develops a child's ability to think outside of the box.

Start off creative and analytical thinking in your children early. This is one area of thought and extrapolation that artificial intelligence will never be able to replicate. With automation rapidly replacing a predicted 30% of all jobs in the future, teaching your children the benefits of lateral thinking skills will make them an indispensable asset in the workforce.

It is easy to make thinking outside of the box teaching and exercises part of your family's daily life. Provide your children with challenges that need brain power to solve. When your kids have to puzzle over a riddle or brain teaser, it is actually helping them to see things in a different light and a different point of view.

All kids need to develop the ability to think outside all the boxes to access to creative play with an adult to guide and help coax them to the correct conclusion.

Here is a great selection of the best "think outside the box" riddles for children.

1. *Draw a line.*
    Now, without touching it,
    how can you make that line longer?

2. *It is possible for a leopard to change its spots.*
    How?

3. *Roger's parents have 3 sons.*
    Their names are Snap, Crackle, and?

4. *Maria has 4 daughters.*
    Each of her daughters has one brother.
    How many children does Maria have?

5. *If a man, a woman,*
    and 2 little dogs are under an umbrella,
    and there is only space under the umbrella
    for one person and one dog,
    why did no one get wet?

6. *There was a train crash.*
    Every single person died.
    Who survived?

7. *What cheese type is made backwards?*

8. *Why is a ghost so bad at telling a lie?*

9. *Name 2 things that you will never be able to*
    eat for your breakfast?

10. Why did Mickey Mouse take a rocket ship into space?

11. What has wings and also a tail.
    Across the skies is where they sail.
    It has no ears or eyes or mouth,
    Yet it still flies round from north to south.

12. A woman is sitting in her house.
    It's nighttime, and no lights are on inside the house.
    There is no lamp or candle or flashlight where
    the woman is sitting.
    And yet she is able to read. How is this possible?

13. What always goes around the wood,
    and yet it never goes inside the wood?

14. Why is Europe like your breakfast frying pan?

15. One bucket holds 5 liters of water.
    Another bucket holds 3 liters of water.
    You have no other way of measuring.

    How can you fill the 5 liters bucket with exactly
    4 gallons of water?

16. The more of these you take,
    the more you are leaving behind.

17. I give beautiful white creamy milk,
    and I also have a horn.
    Yet I am not a cow.
    What am I?

18. What is lighter than a feather.
    Yet the strongest person in the world can't hold
    this thing for more than 5 minutes?

19. A truck delivery person is going opposite the
    flow of traffic in a 1-way street,
    and yet they aren't stopped by the police.
    Why is this?

20. What is a word that has 5 letters,
    but it sounds as though it only has 1?

21. What is begins and ends in "T"
    and also has it inside?

22. What amazing invention allows you
    To see right through walls?

23. Try to say racing car backwards.

24. Until you measure me,
    I am unknown.
    Why is it that you miss me when
    I have flown?

25. Lizzie's mother has 5 children.
    The first 4 kids are named Baba, Bebe, Bibi, and Bobo.
    So, what is the name of kid number five?

26. Which way should I say this?
    The egg yolk is white,
    or the egg yolk is white?

27. *The more I will be,*
    the less you see.
    What am I?

28. *What can be found in*
    Saturn, Jupiter, Mercury, Earth, and Mars,
    but not in Neptune or Venus?

29. *These things love food but*
    hate water.

30. *There are 3 houses.*
    The first house is painted red.
    The second house is painted green.
    The third house is painted white.
    The red house is on the right-side of the house that
    is to be found in the middle.
    The little green house is on the right of the house in
    the middle.
    So, where is the white house?

31. *It is at the very center of gravity.*
    You can also find it on Venus.
    But somehow, it's not found on Mars.
    What is it?

32. *Which one travels faster.*
    Heat or cold?

33. A man is walking in the rain.
    There is no shelter on the side of the road.
    He has no hood, hat, or umbrella.
    When he arrives at his destination,
    he is completely soaked except for the fact that
    not one single hair on his head is wet.
    How is this possible?

34. A cowboy rides into a desert Western town on Friday.
    He stays in town for only 3 days,
    and then he rides back out of town on Friday.
    How is this possible?

35. 2 boxers are in a boxing match which is scheduled
    to run for 12 rounds.
    After only 6 rounds,
    1 of the boxers gets knocked out cold.
    Yet no man has thrown a punch.
    How is this possible?

36. A father and son are involved in a car accident.
    They are both injured and taken to separate hospitals.
    When the boy is taken into surgery
    to have his injuries fixed,
    the surgeon says:

    "It's not possible for me to do this operation
    because this boy is actually my son."
    How is this possible?

37. What word can be used with all of these words:
    Cottage, Swiss, and Cake?

38. *What word can be used with all of these words: Day, screen, and glasses?*

39. *What word can be used with all of these words: Cap, cube, and cream?*

40. *What word can be used with all of these words: Cup, fly, and knife?*

Part 3
Riddles for Adults

Riddles for adults are just as fun as they are for kids. We find riddles a delightful way to pass the time and to entertain ourselves because they make our brains work a little harder. Then there is the big reveal when someone tells everyone the answer. It makes everything so much clearer, and then we have the pleasure of going out and telling the riddle to someone else.

Riddles are not at all like jokes. A joke is told to make people laugh, and a riddle is told to make people think. When someone knows the end or punchline of a joke, it ruins the fun for them. But when you already know the answer to a riddle, or have even been able to work it out, it is a treat to be able to sit back and watch the others in the room thinking hard to try and solve it.

The asking and answering of riddles is something we have grown up with as children. Gollum and his riddles in the dark with Bilbo Baggins in The Hobbit book (part of the Lord of the Rings book series); Batman and his arch enemy, The Riddler; and the Harry Potter book series referred to at the beginning of this Riddles Bundle: they all give us a thrill when we can work out the answer before the hero manages to do so!

This adult preoccupation with riddles is a feature used by detective novels to keep the reader interested in who did the crime. These books are called "Whodunnits?" These books sell like hot cakes because one of the best parts of reading them is to try and work out who is the perpetrator before it is explained in the novel. Agatha Christie was one of the first authors to bring this style of mystery writing into the mainstream

Riddles are still popular today because they are mini mysteries just waiting to be solved.

Logic Riddles

Riddles that need to be solved with the use of logic have been around for thousands of years. One of the oldest riddles written down in cuneiform says:

> *"Here you enter blind and*
> *leave with sight.*
> *What place am I?"*

The answer is A school.

This indicates that there is a huge amount of hidden meanings and obscure references used in riddling. This is especially true in times gone by when there were no distractions from answering a puzzling question.

Puns, sudoku, crossword puzzles, and quiz show: all of these entertainments play into our love and enjoyment of asking questions, posing a problem, and trying to work out what is the answer.

Edward de Bono is a famous philosopher who believes that lateral thinking can help us solve problems by using a creative and indirect reasoning method – one that is not immediately obvious at first. In his book: Lateral Thinking (1967), de Bono posits the theory that lateral thinking is of more use to us than a traditional step-by-step approach to logic.

Given as an example is King Solomon solving the dilemma of the stolen baby.

Riddles that require logic to be used to solve them are an excellent way to sharpen the mind and use other ways of looking at things.

1. The Intelligent Prince

A royal king insists his daughter, the princess, marries the cleverest of her three princely suitors. So, the court vizier devises a logic riddle to test their intelligence.

The three princes are brought together in one room and seated down facing one another. Then each prince is shown three white caps and two black caps. Servants approach the three princes, and they are blindfolded.

Next, one of the caps from the table is put on top of each prince's head. The remaining caps are taken away and put into another room. Then the court vizier asks prince number one to work out what is the color of his cap. But, he is not allowed to remove his own cap; only look at the color of the cap on the other princes' heads.

If he gets the answer right, he marries the princess and becomes king when the old king dies.

If he gets the answer wrong, he must forfeit his offer of marriage and pay the king one thousand gold ducats.

The same rules are given to the other two princes in their turn. Then all the blindfolds are removed. The first prince sees they other two hesitating answers. They have white caps.

Hint: Based on what you can work out, why are the other two princes hesitating?

You are the first prince. What do you do when you see somehow that the other two princes are wearing white caps? You see the other two princes hesitate to make an answer. Is it because they are afraid of getting it wrong, unwilling to guess, or too stupid to work this riddle out?

This is confusing to you as the first prince because you know that the other two princes are very clever. You also have a deep understanding are both in love with the princess and really want to be her husband and become king.

And yet the king whispered to each prince before entering the room that this test was about intelligence and also bravery.

What do you say is the color of your cap now?

> *The answer:* The grand vizier would never have se-
> lected two white caps and then one black cap. This
> would mean that the two other princes would be see-
> ing one black cap and one white cap. You would defi-
> nitely be put at a serious drawback if you were the
> only person to be wearing a black cap.

If you are the one person wearing a black cap, then it wouldn't be long before one of the other princely suitors worked out they have a white cap.

If you were to see one white and one black cap being worn in front of you, you would know that the grand vizier would never choose two black caps and one white cap as the prince that is seeing only two black caps in front of him would have immediately shouted out *The The answer:* and not sat there hesitating.

Thus, the answer in a fair test of intelligence could only be if all three princes are wearing white caps. After giving some time for the other princes to act first, it is quite safe to say out loud that you, prince number one, are wearing a white cap.

2. The One Hundred Gold Coins

Five bold pirates have boarded a galleon ship and now have a treasure of one hundred gold coins. Now, they have to divide up their loot.

- Each pirate is very clever

- Each pirate is sneaky and treacherous

- Each pirate is selfish

However, no one in the crew is more clever, treacherous, and selfish than the captain.

The captain speaks out with a proposal as to how to divide up the loot. Everyone in the crew as to vote on his proposal. If half or more of the pirate crew say, "Aye," then the loot is divvied up as per the proposal. This is wise because no clever pirate would be content to go against the captain if they didn't maybe also have a majority of superior crew force on their side.

If the captain's proposal fails to get the support of half the crew at least, including the captain himself, he faces the prospect of his crew mutinying. The majority will turn against the poor guy and might even make him walk the wooden plank. The pirates will simply begin dividing up the loot again once the captain has walked the plank.

What is the absolute maximum count of gold coins the pirate captain can retain, without the possibility of his crew mutinying and making the captain walk the plank?

Hint: Say there are two pirates, who then lose out by having the fewest gold coins? Say there are three pirates, who then lose out by having the fewest amount of gold coins? Say there are four pirates, who then lose out by having the fewest coins?

The answer: The captain makes the decision to keep 98 gold coins for himself. Then he gives one gold coin to the pirate who is his third-in-command, third in seniority to himself. And then the captain gives one gold coin to the pirate who is the most junior in the crew.

This is his reasoning.

If there were two pirates, the captain would simply go ahead and vote for himself to get all the loot as this decision would count for 50% of this required vote.

If there were three pirates in the crew, the third pirate would have to sway at least one other pirate to join him in his vote. When the remaining pirate realizes the vote is going against him, he will join in with the plan, or else he knows he will get nothing.

Say there are only four pirates. Pirate number four would give one gold coin to the captain, again because he knows he will get nothing if he doesn't give the captain 50% of the vote.

Thus, when there are five pirates, the third-in-command and the most junior pirates vote for the captain's plan and receive one gold coin each because they know the alternate is to risk walking the plank or getting nothing.

The Three Sleepy Greek Philosophers

On a sunny day, three sleepy Greek philosophers were sitting under the shadow of a grove of olive and cedar trees. They uncorked a bottle of retsina and then began to philosophize about the existence of life.

After a lengthy discourse, they fell asleep.

While the three Greek philosophers slept, the three owls who had been sitting in the tree branches above their heads continued the discourse.

When the three owls had finished their own discussion, each owl dropped something onto each Greek philosophers' head. Then they flew away to the next olive grove with a soft hoot.

Maybe it was the hooting or the plop of what the owls had dropped on their heads, but the three Greek philosophers awoke. They all looked around at each other, and then suddenly they all began to shout out with loud laughter. Then, suddenly, one of the philosophers stopped laughing abruptly.

Why was this?

> **Hint:** The one philosopher who abruptly stopped laughing had asked himself why the other two were laughing and what were they laughing at.

> *The answer:* The philosopher stopped laughing as the realization dawned on him that if he had nothing at all on his head, then the 2nd cleverest sleepy Greek philosopher would have immediately deduced that

the 3rd philosopher was only laughing at himself. And then, in turn, the 2nd philosopher would have stopped laughing. This meant that every one of them must have had owl dropping on his head, and that's not funny. But it's a fairly good assumption about the existence of life.

Trick Questions

1. How can you manage to make the
   number "one" completely disappear?

2. Count the seconds you can find in one calendar year?

3. What thing has four fingers, and also a thumb.
   But it isn't alive or human?

4. This is usually given, but almost never taken.
   Yet, everyone needs it. What could this thing be?

5. This has four legs, one head, and one foot so what is it?

6. What is never seen in a day, but you can see it
   once in a year and also twice in a week?

7. What has an eye, but still can't see?

8. When you need this thing, you throw it away,
   and when you don't even need it anymore,
   then you bring it back. What is it?

9. The person who makes it doesn't even need it.
   The person who buys doesn't want to use it.
   The person who ends up using it doesn't even
   know they have. What is it?

10. I am a stone inside of a tree.
    I will help your words to outlive thee.
    If you move me, I stand.
    The more I stand to be used, the less of me I am.
    What am I?

11. *If you have three of these, you have three.*
    If you have two of these, you have two.
    But, if you have only one of these, then you have none.
    What are they?

12. *A person enters a hardware store in town.*
    They ask the store clerk,
    "How much are these things?"

    The hardware store clerk replies,
    "Five dollars apiece, please."
    The person then says,

    "Great. Then I'll have 99 for myself.
    And then 100 for my neighbor."
    The hardware store clerk replies,
    "Thank you. That will be twenty-five dollars."
    What on earth is going on?

13. *There's a really famous rock group.*
    All four of the members are dead.
    But one of the rock group members was actually
    assassinated. Can you remember the name of
    this rock group?

14. *A peacock lays its eggs on the chain-link*
    the fence between two neighbors' houses.
    Who ends up owning the eggs?

15. *What is the one thing that nobody wants,*
    but somehow everybody wants to win?

Riddles to Make You Think
Outside the Box

1. What is more evil than the Devil,
    yet is greater than God?
    Rich people want it, but only poor people have it.

    If you eat only this, you will die!
    What is this?

2. Name three days in consecutive order without
    using the words: Sunday, Friday,
    or Wednesday.

3. What can everyone make, and yet no one can see?

4. I have teeth, but I still can't chew. So, what am I?

5. What bird can lift the most weight without
    dropping it?

6. How much soil is in a hole five feet wide,
    five feet in length, and five feet in depth?

7. What has three feet, and can't walk or hobble?

8. Name four days in the week that begins
    with the letter "T."

9. *A person leaves home.*
    Then they take three left turns and return straight
    home. When they get there,
    they find two people wearing masks.

    Where is each one of these 3 people situated?
    They are on a baseball field and the
    two people in masks are the umpire and the catcher.

10. *What gains in size the more you subtract from it?*

11. *What is nowhere and everywhere?*
    What is right in front of you,
    and yet you will never see it.
    Wherever you go, it will be there.
    But if you go without it, you will die.
    What is it?

12. *What is rarely touched, yet it is often held?*
    And if you are clever, you use it well.

13. *You stand in front of 2 golden gates,*
    both exactly the same.

    One of the golden gates leads up to heaven.
    The other golden gate leads down to hell.
    At each golden gate stands a gatekeeper.
    One gatekeeper for each gate.

    You know that one of the gatekeepers always
    speaks the absolute truth.

You also know that the other gatekeeper always lies.
However, you don't know which gatekeeper
is the truth teller, and which gatekeeper is the liar.
Which one is guarding which gate?

You are only permitted to ask one gatekeeper one
question. You need to discover which gate is
the gate to heaven.
What is the one question that you ask?

14. An old man owes an evil man a lot of money that
he has no chance of ever repaying.
The evil man says to the old man,
"If you give me your daughter to be my wife,
I will forgive you for your debt to me."

The old man tells his daughter about this offer.
She agrees that it is the only solution she can
think of to settle her father's debt.

But, she hates the evil man and
doesn't want to marry him.
She proposes the following solution.
"I will agree to this proposal if

I am given a 50/50 chance.
Put one black pebble,
and one white pebble into a small sack.

If I pull the black pebble out of the small sack,
I will marry the evil man.

But, if I pull the white pebble out of the sack,
my father's debt is forgiven and
I don't marry the evil man."

When the evil man heard about this counteroffer,
he agreed. The old man's daughter was
very beautiful and and worth the chance of a gamble.

However, the evil man didn't plan on leaving things
in the lap of the gods. So, he added this proviso.
If the daughter ends up refusing to choose a pebble
out of the small sack altogether, the old man and
his daughter must work as slaves in the evil man's
house until the end of their days.

The three participants went to a pebble beach close
by to their town and proceeded to carry out the gamble.
The old man's daughter had very sharp
eyes and she noticed it when the evil man bent down
and picked up two black pebbles from the beach and
put them into the small sack.
What does she do?

15. *A regular bar patron walks quickly into*
    his favorite bar.
    He stops at the bar counter and asks the barman to
    please give him a glass of water.
    The barman instantly pulls out the shotgun
    he keeps underneath the counter,
    and then points it directly at his regular bar patron
    who asked for the glass of water.

    The customer smiles says, "thank you," and calmly
    walks out of the bar again.
    Why is this happening?

"How is This Possible?" Riddles

1. You hold a telescope up to your eye,
   and in your view is a cruise ship full of people.
   But there actually is not a single person on-board
   the cruise ship at all.
   How is this possible?

2. You can hold this without touching it.
   How is this possible?
   The answer: It's a conversation.

3. Two mothers and two daughters visited an
   Italian restaurant and ate one slice of garlic
   bread each.
   But only three slices of garlic bread were eaten
   by them.
   How is this possible?

4. When this is put forwards, it's a ton.
   But when it's backwards, it's not.
   How is this possible?

5. A man gets into the elevator on the top floor of
   the apartment block where he lives and
   travels all the way down to building lobby alone
   every day.
   But when he returns home after work every day,
   he waits in the lobby until someone else comes
   along and needs to use the elevator as well.
   Only then does he get into the elevator and ride
   up to his apartment.
   How is this possible?

6. *I can go up this chimney down.*
   And yet, I cannot go down this chimney up.
   How is this possible?

7. *I can dance without legs.*
   I can breathe without lungs.
   I'm not alive, nor do I live or die.
   Yet, somehow, I manage to do all of these three things.
   How is this possible?

8. *A man builds a completely square house.*
   It has four walls. All four walls are facing south.
   How is this possible?

9. *A young man lies dead in a field.*
   Right next to the corpse is an unopened package,
   closed and untouched.

   There is definitely not anything else in the field.
   There is no other person nearby.
   And yet the young man is dead.
   How is this possible?

10. *There is a huge, red, wooden barn.*
    The barn is completely empty inside except for
    the fact there is a dead man who is hanging
    from the middle, center barn rafter.

    There is a rope around the hanged man's neck.
    The rope is ten feet in length.
    The hanged man's feet are also three feet high off
    the ground.

The closest wall is 20 feet away.
It is impossible to scale the walls or
climb along the barn rafters.
And yet the man managed to hang himself.
How is this possible?

11. Out on the lawn are the following things,
   Five small stones
   One carrot
   One scarf
   One hat
   No one deliberately put these items on the lawn out-
   side, but nobody is surprised to see them there.
   How is this possible?

12. A mother has two sons in the room with her.
   She is very truthful, and she tells everyone
   in the room that her sons were born at the
   exact same hour, and in the same month,
   and also in the same year.

   But her sons are definitely not twins.
   How is this possible?

13. A man stops his car at a hotel.
   Without doing anything else,
   the man immediately realizes that he
   is totally broke and completely bankrupt.
   He hasn't looked at his phone,
   or heard the news or
   seen a banner headline outside the hotel.
   And yet he knows this has happened.
   How is this possible?

14. *A group of archeologists was excavating*
an ancient burial site.
They dug very deep into an unknown part of the site.
Suddenly, their shovels hit something solid.

They cleared away all the soil and rocks around the
solid object and, to their amazement, saw what
looked like a time capsule.
The archeologists were very excited when
they saw what looked like two completely
uncorrupted bodies inside the time capsule.

The two bodies were lying side by side in
a time capsule made of transparent glass.

The archeologists could clearly see inside and
they noticed that the two bodies were naked
and human; one man and one woman.

The archeologists immediately knew the two bodies
were Adam and Eve.
How is this possible?

Remember that during the asking and answering of riddles, the answerer is allowed to ask a reasonable number of questions, and the riddler should try to answer them truthfully.

There aren't any hard and fast rules about how much help someone can give or receive during a riddle test. It's good to bear in mind that if you are the one person with the answers in front of you, it's easy to smile at the other person's incorrect attempts at solving a riddle!

Answers for Part 1
Riddles for Kids from 9-10

Best "What am I?"
Riddles for Family Car Journeys

1. They immediate jump to conclusion is to think about some kind of monster. Hints that can be given are:

   "The clue is the fact that the eye is in a column."

   "And remember that only one of the eyes is red."

   The answer: of course, is a traffic light.

2. The clue that can be given here is:

   "Think about words that signify the opposite of talking."

   The answer: Silence

3. These two "What am I" riddles are linked. There may be some complaints about having to answer two riddles in one, but the answer will soon put a smile back on everyone's faces.

   The answer: Nightfall, and daybreak. You can't have night-break and day-fall!

4. There might be a lot of chatting about what type of food this is. If you are driving through farmlands when you ask this riddle, the answer might just be staring at you straight in the face.

   The answer: An ear of corn.

5. This riddle can appear to be very perplexing, yet when you hear The *The answer:* it will all be suddenly clear. It might seem as though the answer is some mythological creature, but that is wrong.

   The answer: Tomorrow.

6. This is an easy riddle, and a good way to warm a small child to the riddle-playing game.

   The answer: A towel.

7. A great clue to give for this riddle is:

   "What is just below the eyebrows you are frowning with?"

   The answer: Your eye.

8. The best clue for this riddle is:

   "What is the last object you need in your bucket when you're trying to water the garden?"

   The answer: A hole.

9. This is a good riddle to follow on from the previous one as the answer can be more easily deduced by the younger member of the family.

   The The answer: A sponge.

10. Any clues for this riddle will have to focus on geography and nature.

    The answer: A running river.

11. A good clue would be to focus on what blows in the wind.

    The answer: A flag.

12. This is an excellent way to remind children that post offices were once very popular places and used to deliver letters.

    The answer: I'm a post office.

13. Clues can revolve around looking up instead of looking around.

    The answer: I'm a star.

14. The clue for this is not Benjamin Button or a magician!

    The answer: I'm a candle.

15. A good hint for this riddle would be to refer back to the post office riddle.

    The answer: I'm a letter.

16. Hints for this riddle can mention that the child will not want to get into this thing in the first place.

    The answer: I'm in trouble.

17. Hint that there are many things on the dining table that aren't eaten.

    The answer: I am cutlery.

18. Old school message delivery systems are alive and well in Riddle Land.

    The answer: I am a stamp.

19. The answer to this riddle can be changed to whatever singer is most popular at the time.

    The answer: The front row of a K-Pop concert.

20. This is a great riddle to ask on car journeys.

    The answer: I am a scarecrow.

Best Trick Questions for Children

1. *The answer:* An umbrella does!

2. *The answer:* A newspaper!

3. *The answer:* Survivors aren't buried!

4. *The answer:* You have two apples because it isn't $3 - 2 = 1$!

5. *The answer:* Electric trains don't have a smoke!

6. *The answer:* All months have twenty-eight days!

7. *The answer:* They both weigh the same!

8. *The answer:* "Are you asleep?"

9. *The answer:* Holes!

10. *The answer:* Darkness!

Best Brain Teasers for Children

1. *The answer:* No, it's not the natural Landscape Arch in the Arches National Park, Utah, U.S.A. Nor is it the human made Gateway Arch in St. Louis in Missouri, U.S.A. It's a rainbow!

2. *The answer:* It can never get wetter because it is already wet. The ocean, of course!

3. *The answer:* This might keep you guessing for a while, but if you don't manage to work this brainteaser out, you can relax. It's a coin!

4. *The answer:* Cheer up if you have caught this thing. It's cold!

5. *The answer:* Stairs!

6. *The answer:* A promise! Don't break yours!

7. *The answer:* A secret!

8. *The answer:* No, it's not yawning, stretch, or drink something. We all open our eyes!

9. *The answer:* The letter "T"!

10. *The answer:* After telling this brain teaser really fast, so that no one has time to think, the answer is Freddy! Not Four!

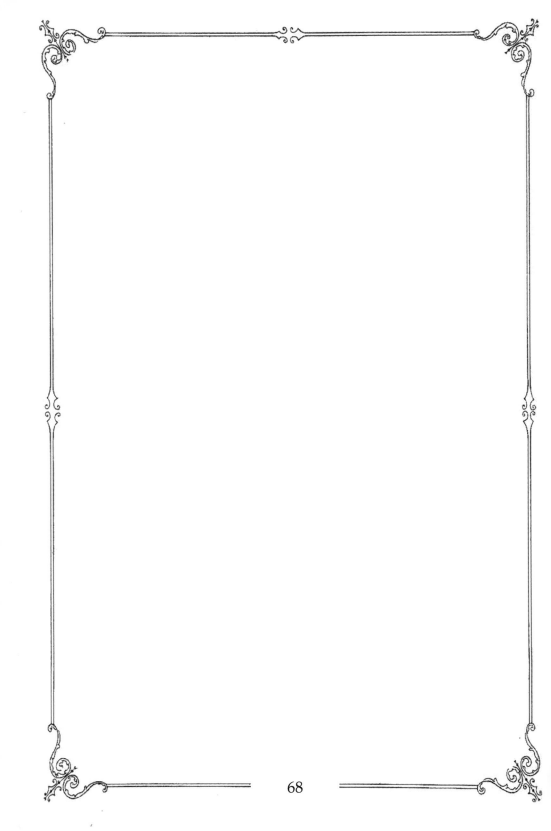

Answers for Part 2
Riddles for Kids from 10-12

Best Riddles for Children
that Will Help Develop Logical Thinking

1. *The answer:* The letter "C".

2. *The answer:* The letter "W".

3. *The answer:* There is no staircase because it's a cottage.

4. *The answer:* A clock.

5. *answer:* An envelope.

6. *answer:* Because they are still alive.

7. *The answer:* An egg.

8. *The answer:* In the dictionary.

9. *The answer:* I am throwing the ball up into the air.

10. *The answer:* A bottle.

11. *The answer:* They did not say anything – instead they just waved.

12. *The answer:* Because he fell off the first step at the bottom.

13. *The answer:* Your own name.

14. *The answer:* Your age.

15. *The answer:* A doorbell ring.

16. *The answer:* Stop thinking.

17. *The answer:* A monkey.

18. *The answer:* A donkey.

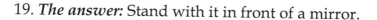

19. *The answer:* Stand with it in front of a mirror.

20. *The answer:* Your shadow.

21. *The answer:* The word that is spelt incorrectly in every English dictionary is "incorrectly," of course.

22. *The answer:* A palm.

23. *The answer:* Yes, anyone can. We sleep at night, not during the day.

24. *The answer:* A piano.

25. *The answer:* A rhino.

26. *The answer:* An elephant's shadow.

27. *The answer:* A horse keeps its shoes on.

28. *The answer:* A book.

29. *The answer:* Your fingers.

30. *The answer:* Your future.

31. *The answer:* On a map.

32. *The answer:* A very sad zebra.

33. *The answer:* The President.

34. *The answer:* Only halfway. Then you are running out of the woods.

35. *The answer:* "M".

36. *The answer:* Seven.

37. Answer. A clock or watch.

38. *The answer:* All greenhouses are made with glass.

39. *The answer:* You lose the pebble.

40. *The answer:* The pebble gets wet.

41. *The answer:* A table has four legs.

42. *The answer:* 9.

43. *The answer:* Oak trees have acorns, not nuts.

44. *The answer:* The word "shorter" – short (5 letters) + "er".

45. *The answer:* Holes.

46. *The answer:* A tennis ball is served.

47. *The answer:* Eggs.

48. *The answer:* The Mississippi River.

49. *The answer:* A dinner plate.

50. *The answer:* Because it is always stuffed.

Best "Think Outside of the Box" Riddles for Children

1. *The answer:* Draw a shorter line underneath it.

2. *The answer:* By the leopard moving from one spot and onto another spot. Now, it has changed spots.

3. *The answer:* Roger.

4. *The answer:* Five. Each of Maria's daughters will have the same brother.

5. *The answer:* Because it was a beach umbrella and it wasn't raining.

6. *The answer:* The couples survived.

7. *The answer:* Edam cheese.

8. *The answer:* Because it's possible to see right through them.

9. *The answer:* Supper and lunch.

10. *The answer:* To visit Pluto.

11. *The answer:* A kite.

12. *The answer:* The lady is blind. She is reading using Braille.

13. *The answer:* Tree bark.

14. *The answer:* Because it has Greece at the very bottom, of course.

15. *The answer:* Empty out the 3-liter bucket. Pour the water from the 5-liter bucket into the 3-liter bucket. Now empty out the water from the liter bucket. Pour the remaining 2 liters of water that's in the 5-liter bucket into the 3-liter bucket. Now fill the 5-liter bucket all the way up again with water. Next, finish filling up the 3-liter bucket to the top. Now your 5-liter bucket will only contain 4 liters of water.

16. *The answer:* Footprints.

17. *The answer:* A milk delivery truck.

18. *The answer:* Breath.

19. *The answer:* Because the truck driver is walking.

20. *The answer:* Queue.

21. *The answer:* A teapot.

22. *The answer:* A window.

23. *The answer:* Racing car backwards.

24. *The answer:* Time.

25. *The answer:* Lizzie.

26. *The answer:* An egg yolk is yellow.

27. *The answer:* Fog.

28. *The answer:* The letter "R".

29. *The answer:* Fire

30. *The answer:* In Washington, D.C.

31. *The answer:* The letter "V".

32. *The answer:* Heat must travel faster because it's possible for you to catch a cold.

33. *The answer:* The man is completely bald.

34. *The answer:* The cowboy's horse is called Friday.

35. *The answer:* The boxers are a woman.

36. *The answer:* The surgeon is the injured boy's mother.

37. *The answer:* Cheese.

38. *The answer:* Sun

39. *The answer:* Ice

40. *The answer:* Butter.

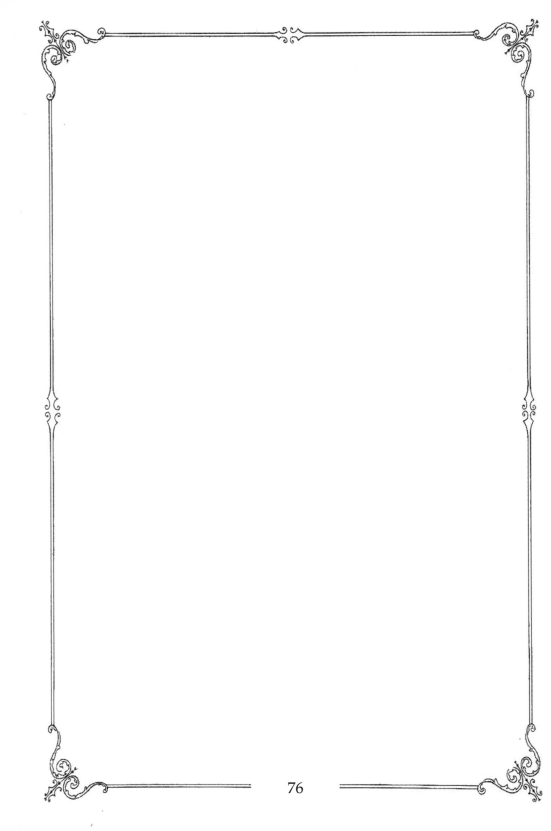

Answers for Part 3
Riddles for Adults

Trick Questions

1. *The answer:* Simply add on a "G" at the very end, and then the "one" is "gone."

2. *The answer:* Twelve seconds. The second of January, the second of February, the second of March. You do the math.

3. *The answer:* Your winter gloves.

4. *The answer:* Advice.

5. *The answer:* A bed.

6. *The answer:* "E"

7. *The answer:* A needle.

8. *The answer:* A boat anchor.

9. *The answer:* A coffin.

10. *The answer:* A pencil.

11. *The answer:* Choices.

12. *The answer:* The person was buying house numbers to put on their post box.

13. *The answer:* Mount Rushmore.

14. *The answer:* No one owns the eggs, because peahens lay eggs, and not peacocks.

15. *The answer:* A lawsuit.

Riddles to Make You Think
Outside the Box

1. *The answer:* Nothing.

2. *The answer:* Yesterday, today, and then tomorrow.

3. *The answer:* Noise.

4. *The answer:* A comb for the hair.

5. *The answer:* A crane.

6. *The answer:* None, the hole is empty.

7. *The answer:* One yardstick.

8. *The answer:* Today, tomorrow, Tuesday, and Thursday.

9. *The answer:* They are on a baseball field, and the two people in masks are the umpire and the catcher.

10. *The answer:* A hole.

11. *The answer:* Oxygen.

12. *The answer:* Your tongue.

13. *The answer:* You approach one gatekeeper at one of the golden gates and ask them the following question.

    Whichever gate the gatekeeper tells you like

    The answer: you will know that that is the way to heaven.

    If you ask your question to heaven's gatekeeper, they will tell you the truth. The truthful gatekeeper knows dishonest gatekeeper is going to lie, so they will show you the gate that leads to heaven.

If asked that question to the gatekeeper who the liar is, they will lie with their answer and in this lie, show you the gate to heaven.

Another way to answer this riddle: Ask one of the gatekeepers, "Does the gate guard at the gate to heaven always speak the truth, tell me?"

If the gate guard says, "No." then the other golden gate is the way to heaven. If the gate guard says, "Yes." Then the gate they are guarding is the gate to heaven.

14. *The answer:* The old man's daughter puts her hand into the small sack, picks out a pebble, and withdraws her hand with the pebble closed up tightly in her fist. They are still on the pebble beach, and she tosses the pebble that is in her fist as far away as she can. When they ask her what color, pebble did she have in her fist, she replies, "Look inside the sack. Whichever color pebble still remains, then I must have picked the other color pebble."

15. *The answer:* The man who walked into the bar had hiccups. The barman was trying to give him a big fright so that the hiccups would go away. They did, and the customer was happy and left.

"How is This Possible?" Riddles

1. *The answer:* Everyone on-board the cruise ship is married.

2. *The answer:* It's a conversation.

3. *The answer:* This is the group. One grandmother, who is mother to the other mother. And her daughter who has a daughter of her own. Grandmother, plus daughter, who has her own daughter equals two mothers and two daughters.

4. *The answer:* It's a ton.

5. *The answer:* He's a little person. He can easily reach the button that is at the very bottom of the elevator controls that takes him down all the way to the lobby. But he can't reach the button at the very top of the controls that take him back up to his apartment at the top.

6. *The answer:* I'm an umbrella.

7. *The answer:* I am a fire.

8. *The answer:* The man has built the house exactly on the North Pole.

9. *The answer:* The young man is a parachutist, and the package is his unopened parachute. The parachute failed to open, so the young man lies dead with his unopened parachute equipment next to him.

10. *The answer:* The man climbed onto a big block of ice, and the ice has now melted.

11. *The answer:* They have been left behind when a snowman melted.

12. *The answer:* The two sons in the room with the mother are two sons from a set of male triplets.

13. *The answer:* The man is playing the game, Monopoly.

14. *The answer:* The man and the women were Adam and Eve because they didn't have belly buttons.

Disclaimer

The opinions and ideas of the author contained in this publication are designed to educate the reader in an informative and helpful manner. While we accept that the instructions will not suit every reader, it is only to be expected that the recipes might not gel with everyone. Use the book responsibly and at your own risk. This work with all its contents does not guarantee correctness, completion, quality or correctness of the provided information. Always check with your medical practitioner should you be unsure whether to follow a low carb eating plan. Misinformation or misprints cannot be completely eliminated. Human error is real!

Designer: Oliviadesign

Picture: pikselstock // shutterstock.com

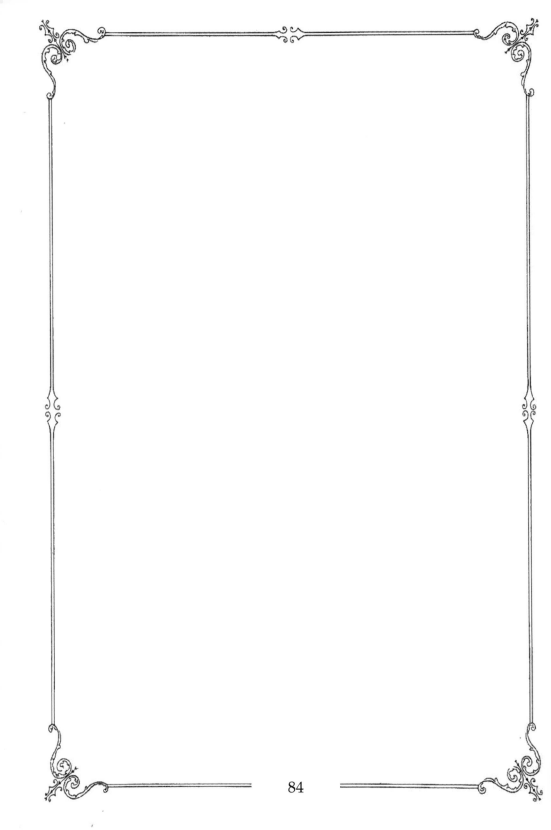

Printed in Great Britain
by Amazon